P9-BYH-941

The BATHROOM TRIVIA QUIZ BOOK

———— • ————

by

Russ Edwards & Jack Kreismer

RED-LETTER PRESS, INC.
Saddle River, New Jersey

THE BATHROOM TRIVIA QUIZ BOOK

COPYRIGHT ©2011 Red-Letter Press, Inc.

ISBN-13: 978-1-60387-002-3
ISBN-10: 1-60387-002-4

All Rights Reserved

Printed in the United States of America
For information address:

Red-Letter Press, Inc.
P.O. Box 393
Saddle River, NJ 07458

www.Red-LetterPress.com

ACKNOWLEDGMENTS

EDITORIAL:
Jeff Kreismer

•

BOOK DESIGN AND TYPOGRAPHY:
Matt Taets

•

COVER:
Behum Graphics

•

PROJECT DEVELOPMENT:
Kobus Reyneke

The BATHROOM TRIVIA QUIZ BOOK

RED-LETTER PRESS, INC.
Saddle River, New Jersey

Story Time

1. How many stories does the Leaning Tower of Pisa have?

2. This 1961 film won ten out of eleven Oscar nominations and was a Broadway hit as well.

3. Tom Hanks and Tim Allen were two of the voices in this 1995 computer-animated flick.

4. Jacob and Wilhelm were brothers who published short stories under their last name. What was it?

5. Le Pays des Contes de Fées is the Paris version of the Disneyland ride in California, a canal boat ride through what attraction?

6. From WWII up until his death in 2009, commentator Paul Harvey had a radio feature with a surprise ending followed by his signature signoff, "And now you know...." what?

7. NBC-TV cut off a NY Jets–Oakland Raiders football game in 1968 with 65 seconds left to play in order to present a two-hour version of a classic children's story. The contest became infamously known by what name?

8. Ali MacGraw and Ryan O'Neal starred in this 1970 romantic drama film written by Erich Segal.

9. The 1933 *Three Little Pigs* Disney cartoon was the first to use this method of illustrations or images to pre-conceive a motion picture.

10. *Love Story* was the lead single from this country pop star's *Fearless* album.

Answers

1. Eight
2. *West Side Story*
3. *Toy Story*
4. Grimm, as in *Grimm's Fairy Tales*
5. Storybook Land
6. The Rest of the Story
7. The Heidi Game- The Jets were leading by three points with little more than a minute to play. Infuriated fans missed Oakland's comeback, as they scored 14 points to win, 43-32.
8. *Love Story*
9. Storyboards
10. Taylor Swift

Thoughts of the Throne

"The best measure of a man's honesty isn't his income tax return. It's the zero adjust on his bathroom scale."

– Arthur C. Clarke

Fowl Play

1. Colonel Sanders, the founder of Kentucky Fried Chicken, was born in Indiana. True or False?
2. Donald Duck's nephews were Huey, Dewey and Louie. What were his nieces' names?
3. And what is the middle name of The Donald (Duck, that is)?
4. Is a group of geese called a gander or a gaggle?
5. Benjamin Franklin proposed that this bird be the symbol of the United States rather than the eagle.
6. What's the name of the rooster on the Kellogg's Cornflakes box?
7. Can a chicken fly?
8. Which egg spins easily: a hard cooked or a raw one?
9. Those flaps of flesh that dangle under a chicken's chin are called:
   a) wattles b) jangles c) tittles d) vittles
10. Who is Ted Giannoulas in chicken lore?

Answers

1. True
2. April, May and June
3. Fauntleroy
4. Gaggle
5. Turkey
6. Cornelius
7. Yes, but not very far. According to the International Chicken Flying Association, the record is 542 feet, nine inches. *Guinness* says it's less than that, 301.5 feet, according to their records. And the longest recorded time in the air is 13 seconds.
8. Hard cooked- The moving liquids in a raw egg cause it to wobble.
9. A
10. He's the San Diego Chicken, aka the Famous Chicken, a mascot among mascots who helped them to become widespread throughout professional sports, particularly Major League Baseball.

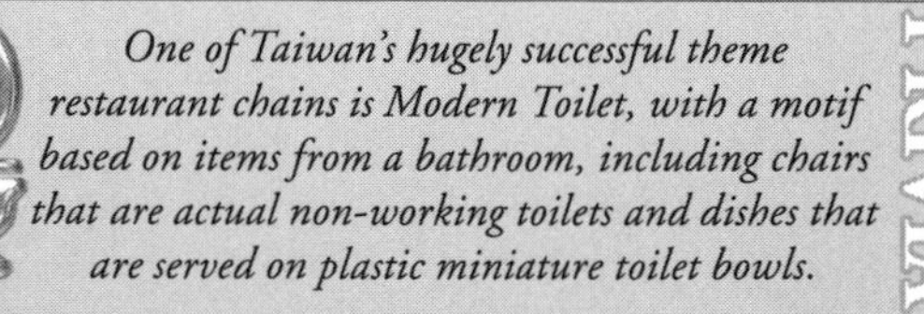

Celebrity Name Game

Celebrities aren't like the rest of us. Sometimes they're not only odd, they want to pass their oddness down to posterity. Match the celeb couple to the unusual names of their offspring.

1. Sean Penn and Robin Wright
2. Chris Martin and Gwyneth Paltrow
3. Alice and Sheryl Cooper
4. Arthur Ashe and Jeanne Moutoussamy
5. Alec Baldwin and Kim Basinger
6. Frank Zappa
7. Sylvester Stallone and Sasha Czack
8. Will Smith and Jada-Pinkett Smith
9. Penn Jillette
10. Forest Whitaker

a. Calico

b. Camera

c. Hopper

d. Moon Unit

e. Ocean

f. Ireland

g. Willow Camille Reign

h. Moxie Crimefighter

i. Sage Moonblood

j. Apple

Answers

1. C (And that's where their marriage went shortly thereafter.)
2. J
3. A
4. B
5. F
6. D (He's also the father of Dweezil and Diva Muffin.)
7. I
8. G
9. H
10. E

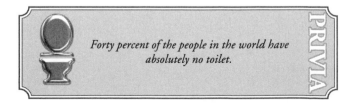

Forty percent of the people in the world have absolutely no toilet.

TRIVIA

ANIMAL INSTINCT

1. What is the only animal with four knees?
2. A full grown bear can run as fast as a(n):
   a) dog b) coyote c) horse d) ostrich
3. Where would you find stripes on tigers- on the skin or on the fur?
4. What Disney dog was originally called Rover?
5. An albatross often does this while it flies.
6. Paper Kite, Sailor, Blue Striped Crow and Julia are all varieties of what?
7. What speed distinction does the spiny tailed iguana hold?
8. What marine animals hold hands while they sleep so as not to drift away from each other?
9. What is the only animal born with horns?
10. Which can dive deeper- a multi-billion dollar nuclear submarine or a sperm whale?

Answers

1. An elephant
2. C- What this means is that if you're out camping with your buddy and you are set upon by a bear, don't bother trying to outrun it. All you have to do is outrun your buddy.
3. Both
4. Pluto
5. It sleeps.
6. Butterflies
7. It's the fastest reptile in the world.
8. Sea Otters
9. The giraffe
10. The sperm whale wins fins down. Although submarine specs are classified, enough is known to say the whale can go about three times deeper.

Thoughts of the Throne

"My roommate says, 'I'm going to take a shower and shave, does anyone need to use the bathroom?' It's like some weird quiz where he reveals the answer first."

– Mitch Hedberg

QUOTE, UNQUOTE

"Based on what you know about him in history books, what do you think Abraham Lincoln would be doing if he were alive today? (1) Writing his memoirs of the Civil War. (2) Advising the President. (3) Desperately clawing at the inside of his _ _ _ _ _ _."
–Late night TV host David Letterman

Complete the above quote by filling in the last word. Its correlating letters can be obtained by answering the following TV questions.

Jay Leno, the host of *The Tonight Show*, is the chief competition for *The Late Show with David Letterman*. Who hosted *The Tonight Show* before Leno?

_ _ _ _ _   _'_ _ _ _ _
6

Who was named the anchor of the *CBS Evening News* in 2011?

_ _ _ _ _   _ _ _ _ _ _
2

What sitcom's theme song was *Where Everybody Knows Your Name*?

"_ _ _ _ _ _"
1

He's the creator of *Jeopardy!*. And the question is, Who is_______?

_ _ _ _   _ _ _ _ _ _ _
3 4

Its oldest winner, at the age of 29, was Taylor Hicks.

_ _ _ _ _ _ _ _   _ _ _ _
5

___ ___ ___ ___ ___ ___
1 2 3 4 5 6

Answers

1. Conan O'Brien
2. Scott Pelley
3. *Cheers*
4. Merv Griffin
5. *American Idol*

Solution: "Based on what you know about him in history books, what do you think Abraham Lincoln would be doing if he were alive today? (1) Writing his memoirs of the Civil War. (2) Advising the President. (3) Desperately clawing at the inside of his **coffin.**"

The Writing On The Wall

Over a men's room mirror:

Express Lane: Five beers or less.

Fun 'n' Games

1. Are there more holes on a Chinese checkerboard or squares on a Scrabble board?
2. How many chess pieces are in a chess set?
3. What question and answer game did Chris Haney and Scott Abbott invent on a rainy Saturday in Montreal in 1979?
4. How many holes does a Wiffle Ball have?
5. How many eyes are there on the four jacks in a deck of cards?
6. What's the standard pitching distance in a game of horseshoes?
7. What popular board game is also known as Draughts?
8. Who's the current host of the longest-running game show in TV history, *The Price Is Right*?
9. Here's a gimme: What's the only sport where the defense has the ball?
10. What three sporting events can you win by going backwards?

Answers

1. Squares on a Scrabble board, 225 - A Chinese checkerboard has 121 holes.
2. 32 (Sixteen for each player.)
3. Trivial Pursuit
4. Eight
5. 12 (a total of four on the one-eyed jacks and eight on the other two jacks)
6. 40 feet for men, 30 for women and juniors
7. Checkers
8. Drew Carey
9. Baseball (or softball)
10. Rowing, the backstroke and tug of war

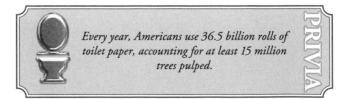

Every year, Americans use 36.5 billion rolls of toilet paper, accounting for at least 15 million trees pulped.

PRIVIA

The Price is Right

Decide whether the figure representing the statement for each of the items listed here is too high, too low or just right.

1. A ticket to the most expensive seat in the house for Super Bowl I in 1967 was $25.
2. Edgar Allan Poe received $500 from *The New York Mirror* for *The Raven* when it was published in 1845.
3. The first Ford Mustang in 1964 was priced at $2,368.
4. George Washington's salary as the first President of the U.S. was $10,000.
5. The cost of a Barbie doll when it was introduced in 1959 was $6.99.
6. The price of a ticket to Woodstock in 1969 was $6.00.
7. Alaska was purchased from Russia in 1867 for two cents per acre.
8. Elvis Presley's American Express credit card went to the highest bidder at a 1994 auction for $94,000.
9. A three-minute phone call from New York to Los Angeles in 1917 was $1.25.
10. A first class postage stamp in 1972 went for ten cents.

Answers

1. Too high- The highest-priced ticket was only $12.
2. Too high- Poe received $10. Allowing for inflation, that's still less than $200 by today's standards.
3. The Price is Right (700,000 models were sold that first year.)
4. Too low- Washington's pay was $25,000.
5. Too high- Barbie could be had for $3.00.
6. The Price is Right, but at one point when the crowds got out of control, folks were let in for free.
7. The Price is Right
8. The Price is Right (and the bidder was highly disappointed that the card had been de-activated)
9. Too low- It was $20.70!
10. Too high- It was eight cents.

The Writing On The Wall

If life is a waste of time, and time is a waste of life, then let's all get wasted and have the time of our lives.

Name's the Same

1. Five surnames have been shared by U.S. presidents. How many can you name?
2. Mets fans in 1962 saw the worst baseball team in history, 40-120. They also saw double with Bob Miller. How so?
3. He was a *Seinfeld* star and his same name counterpart was the former husband of Britney Spears.
4. He was a Hall of Fame baseball player and a down and out homeless broadcaster, given a second chance in 2011.
5. It's the largest city in Maine and in Oregon.
6. Major League Baseball and the National Football League have two teams that share the same nickname. What are they?
7. He was a U.S. president and a third baseman for the old Washington Senators. (Both occupied their positions at the same time!)
8. He's a big name way up north and also a small town in Indiana.
9. He was a comedic actor on the sitcom *Good Times* and was the mayor of New York City.
10. He was a shoeless baseball player and and his same name partner is the father of LaToya.

Answers

1. Adams, Bush, Roosevelt, Johnson and Harrison
2. There were two Bob Millers on the team, both pitchers.
3. Jason Alexander
4. Ted Williams
5. Portland
6. Cardinals and Giants
7. John Kennedy
8. Santa Claus
9. Jimmy Walker
10. Joe Jackson

Thoughts of the Throne

"I found out why cats drink out of the toilet. My mother told me it's because the water is cold in there. And I'm like, 'How did my mother know that?'"

– Wendy Liebman

Claim to Fame Match Game

Match these people with their claims to fame.

1. Isaiah Mustafa	a) *Mad Libs* co-creators
2. Pattie Mallette	b) Tom Thumb's wife
3. Leonard Stern and Roger Price	c) FedEx founder
4. CPT Hanson Crockett Gregory	d) The Old Spice Guy
5. Nadya Suleman	e) Amelia Earhart's co-pilot
6. Fred Smith	f) Doughnut hole inventor
7. Lavinia Warren	g) Justin Bieber's mother
8. Fred Noonan	h) Google co-founders
9. Larry Page and Sergey Brin	i) *Mad* magazine creator
10. Harvey Kurtzman	j) Octomom

Answers

1. D
2. G
3. A
4. F
5. J
6. C
7. B
8. E
9. H
10. I

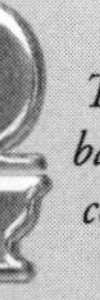

The average person will spend three years in the bathroom in a lifetime. That's nothing when you compare it to the nine years spent watching TV.

By the Numbers

1. How long is a bowling lane?
2. How many toes does a normal cat have?
3. What telephone prefix is used for TV and movies and will always give you a wrong number?
4. What is the only number that is twice the sum of its digits?
5. How many hearts are there on the six of hearts?
6. How many U.S. state capitals are named after U.S. presidents?
7. What's the code name for Coca Cola's secret ingredient?
8. How many nines are there between 1 and 100?
9. How many states border on the Pacific Ocean?
10. How many words were said in Mel Brooks' *Silent Movie*?

Answers

1. 60 feet
2. 18- five on each of the front paws, four on the hind paws
3. 555
4. 18
5. 8
6. 4- Jackson, Mississippi; Jefferson City, Missouri; Lincoln, Nebraska; Madison, Wisconsin
7. 7X
8. 20
9. 5- Did you forget Alaska and Hawaii?
10. 1- "Non," uttered by legendary mime Marcel Marceau

The Writing On The Wall

Here I sit, my dignity tarnished.

The toilet seat was freshly varnished.

ANIMAL ACTS

1. We'll start you off with this doggone quiz by throwing you a bone: What was the name of Dorothy's dog in *The Wizard of Oz*?

2. What's the name of the dog on the Cracker Jack box?

3. In which film would you find Pongo and Perdita?

4. What was the name of the Taco Bell Chihuahua that also played Bruiser's mom in *Legally Blonde II*?

5. Name the three-headed dog that guarded the Philosopher's Stone at Hogwarts in the *Harry Potter* films.

6. What's the name of President Obama's Portuguese Water Dog?

7. What breed of dog starred in the *Beethoven* series?

8. What dog was the first animal to be named to the Animal Hall of Fame in 1969?

9. Andy, Marbles, Rover, Olaf and Spike were his brothers, Belle and Molly his sisters. The dog?

10. Paul McCartney's Old English sheepdog was immortalized in The Beatles' song, *Martha, My Dear.* What was the dog's name?

Answers

1. Toto- The terrier's real name in dog life was Terry.
2. Bingo
3. *101 Dalmatians*
4. Gidget
5. Fluffy
6. Bo
7. Saint Bernard
8. Lassie
9. Snoopy
10. C'mon now… If you didn't get that one, Rin Tin Tin's rolling over in his grave, which, as any hardcore trivia buff knows, is in a renowned pet cemetery in the Parisian suburb of Asnieres-sur-Seine. The famed dog's owner arranged to have Rin Tin Tin returned to his country of birth after the canine celebrity's death at the age of 14 in 1932.

Statistics show that about 72.4% of people place their toilet paper on the roll with the loose end over the top of the roll, facing the user.

PRIVIA

Book Talk

1. Sixteen publishers turned down this girl's journal, including one who said, "The girl doesn't, it seems to me, have a special perception of feeling which would lift that book above the 'curiosity' level." This oft-rejected work was eventually published under what name?

2. True or false? You can't copyright a book title.

3. Ernest Vincent Wright wrote a 50,000 word novel, *Gadsby*, without ever using the most common letter in the English language. What is it?

4. True or false? *Gone with the Wind* was the only novel that Margaret Mitchell ever wrote.

5. Eric Blair wrote *Animal Farm* and *Nineteen Eighty-Four*. What is his more common pen name?

6. Look at the copyright page at the front of this book for its ISBN number. What does ISBN stand for?

7. "Call me Ishmael" is the opening line to what Herman Melville book?

8. What is the right hand page of an open book called?

9. "Patience" and "Fortitude" are the names of the landmark lions which stand in front of what building?

10. Who is the world's first billionaire author?

Answers

1. *The Diary of Anne Frank*
2. True
3. The letter E
4. True
5. George Orwell
6. International Standard Book Number
7. *Moby-Dick*
8. It's called the recto. (The left hand page is the verso.)
9. The New York Public Library
10. J.K. Rowling, author of the *Harry Potter* series

Thoughts of the Throne

"You do live longer with bran, but you spend the last fifteen years on the toilet."

– Alan King

Happy Days

1. In Puerto Rico this children's fast food is known as Cajita Feliz. In Portugal, it's McLanche Feliz. What is it called in the U.S.?

2. Featured in the Tom Cruise flick *Cocktail*, this 1988 hit by Bobby McFerrin became the first a cappella song to top the Billboard Hot 100 chart.

3. Composed by sisters Mildred and Patty Hill in 1893, it's the most recognized song in the English language.

4. It's located in the Amarillo metropolitan area of the Lone Star State and is known as "the town without a frown".

5. You've probably got to be a Baby Boomer to get this one. What was the theme song of the cowboy TV program *The Roy Rogers Show*?

6. Name the 2006 animated movie about a penguin that couldn't sing, but could tap dance something fierce!

7. What song from Broadway's *Bye Bye Birdie* urges you to "brush off the clouds and cheer up"?

8. Artist Harvey Ball was paid $45 in 1963 when he created this international icon.

9. What phrase's origin comes from a certain mollusk's state of mind at high tide, when it's almost impossible to find and thus in no danger of being made into a meal?

10. Which one of Snow White's seven dwarfs does not have a beard?

Answers

1. McDonald's Happy Meal (The Spanish translation of Cajita Feliz is "Happy little box" and the Portuguese equivalent translates to "Happy McSnack".)
2. *Don't Worry, Be Happy*
3. *Happy Birthday to You*
4. Happy, Texas
5. *Happy Trails to You*
6. *Happy Feet*
7. *Put on a Happy Face*
8. The smiley, or happy face
9. "Happy as a clam." In fact, the phrase was originally "Happy as a clam at high water."
10. Gotcha, if you said Happy. It's Dopey, the youngest one.

A Scott company employee saw a crumpled up roll of toilet paper and recognized its potential for another marketable product- a kind of disposable hand towel- thus the inspiration for paper towels.

PRIVIA

THE ONE AND ONLY

1. What is the only number that has its letters in alphabetical order?

2. Only one animal's evidence is admissible in an American court. Can you name it?

3. Name the only creature on Earth that can twist its head in a complete circle.

4. What's the only X-rated movie to win the Academy Award for best picture?

5. In a Scrabble game, what is the only letter represented by one tile?

6. Who was the only bachelor U.S. president?

7. Name the only former heavyweight boxing champion to be buried at Arlington National Cemetery.

8. What's the only food that never spoils?

9. Only one state in the U.S. has no counties. Which one?

10. What is the only Great Lake that's completely in the United States?

Answers

1. Forty
2. The bloodhound
3. The owl
4. *Midnight Cowboy*, in 1969 (Its rating has since been changed to R.)
5. Q
6. James Buchanan
7. Joe Louis
8. Honey
9. Louisiana- It is subdivided by "parishes."
10. Lake Michigan

Thoughts of the Throne

"Men who consistently leave the toilet seat up secretly want women to get up to go to the bathroom in the middle of the night and fall in."

– Rita Rudner

COLOR MY WORLD

1. What color is a U.S. green card?

2. What color is a zebra's skin?

3. True or False? A shark is color blind.

4. What's the name of the room where guests hang out before they go on a TV talk show?

5. Binney and Smith makes 120 different kinds of them and kids ages 2-8 spend an average of 28 minutes a day using them. What are they?

6. Oprah Winfrey, Whoopi Goldberg and Danny Glover were among the cast in this 1985 Steven Spielberg-directed movie about the problems African-American women faced in the early 1900s.

7. What does ROY G BIV stand for?

8. What are the colors of the five Olympic rings?

9. There are two common colors which have no words that rhyme with them. One is purple. What's the other?

10. What is the most common toothbrush color?

Answers

1. Green, naturally... Well, not so naturally. It was green from 1946 until 1964, then changed colors, becoming yellow until 2010, when it reverted back to green.
2. A zebra's skin is black; its fur is striped.
3. False- And if you ever go swimming in a shark-infested area, whatever you do, don't wear a yellow or orange bathing suit. Sharks have terrific eyesight and find those colors extremely irritating.
4. The greenroom- so designed because the color has a calming effect, encouraging relaxation
5. Crayola crayons
6. *The Color Purple*
7. It is a common acronym to help remember the order of the colors of the rainbow- red, orange, yellow, green, blue, indigo and violet.
8. Every flag of a country participating in the Olympics includes at least one of the following colors: blue, black, red, yellow, and green.
9. Orange
10. Blue

By the Weigh

1. Who was the heaviest President of the United States? (Hint: He also threw out the very first Opening Day baseball in 1909.)

2. Renowned as an artist, scientist, and engineer, he was also an inventor and is credited with developing the bathroom scale around 1500. Can you name him?

3. What former tennis star was hired as a trainer on NBC's reality show *The Biggest Loser*?

4. What is the weight of the shot in the men's shot put?

5. Claiming to have helped humanity lose approximately 12,000,000 pounds, this 5'6" fitness expert owns SLIMMONS, a Beverly Hills facility that has welcomed the overweight since 1974. Who is he?

6. If you stacked up a pound of one-dollar bills, would there be more or less than 500 of them?

7. She weighs 225 tons, stands 111'1" tall, has a 35-foot waist and wears a size 879 shoe. Who is this torch bearer?

8. Brooklyn homemaker Jean Nidetch founded it in 1963. Was it NutriSystem, Jenny Craig or Weight Watchers?

9. In pro boxing, what is the maximum weight for a heavyweight fighter?

10. Ernest Evans' biggest hit record was *The Twist*. You know him better by his weight-related nickname. What is it?

Answers

1. "His Rotundity", William Howard Taft, who was 6'2" and weighed 332 lbs
2. Leonardo da Vinci
3. Anna Kournikova
4. 16 pounds
5. Richard Simmons
6. Less- A dollar bill weighs one gram and there are 454 grams in a pound.
7. The Statue of Liberty
8. Weight Watchers
9. There is no upper limit- The minimum for a heavyweight is 200 lbs.
10. Chubby Checker

The Writing On The Wall

It's hard to make a comeback when you haven't been anywhere.

Jacks of All Trades

1. Name the fitness guru who celebrated his 95th birthday with his new book *Live Young Forever* and who performed his daily exercise routine until the day before he died at the age of 96 in 2011.

2. This fast food chain is headquartered in San Diego, California, where it was founded by Robert O. Peterson in 1951.

3. He committed the first live murder on network television.

4. Known for its square bottles and black labels, this whiskey is produced in Lynchburg, Tennessee.

5. John Ritter played this fictional character in the TV sitcom *Three's Company.*

6. On another sitcom, *Frasier*, Eddie played the best friend of the title character. What was Eddie?

7. He owns three Oscars and, with twelve nominations, is the most nominated male actor in Academy Awards history.

8. They called this right-to-die activist "Dr. Death."

9. It was the title of a 1986 Whoopi Goldberg film as well as a 1968 Rolling Stones hit.

10. The Golden Bear, he's won 18 major golf championships.

Answers

1. Jack LaLanne
2. Jack in the Box
3. Jack Ruby, who murdered Lee Harvey Oswald, the assassin of President John F. Kennedy, in 1963
4. Jack Daniel's
5. Jack Tripper
6. A Jack Russell terrier
7. Jack Nicholson
8. Jack Kevorkian
9. *Jumpin' Jack Flash*
10. Jack Nicklaus

The average male who shaves regularly will use up five months of his life doing so, removing 28 feet of hair.

PRIVIA

Affairs of State

1. What state's coastline is longer than that of all the states' coastlines combined in the U.S.?

2. It's 630 feet by 630 feet and is officially dubbed "The Jefferson National Expansion Monument." Where is it located?

3. What is the southernmost state in the U.S.?

4. We'll give you ten seconds to answer this one- Name the only state that begins with two vowels.

5. What's the only state whose capital is made up of three words?

6. William G. Morgan created a game called "mintonette", later called volleyball, in 1895 in the town of Holyoke, which is located in what state?

7. Carl Magee's 1935 invention and installation of the parking meter was not a welcome attraction to visitors of the Big Friendly, a moniker attributed to the biggest city in what state?

8. The NBA's Los Angeles Lakers got their name from their original home, which was in what state?

9. Where is the Four Corners Monument?

10. What is the most common last letter for a state in the U.S.?

Answers

1. Alaska
2. Missouri- St. Louis, to be exact. It's also known as the Gateway Arch.
3. Hawaii
4. Iowa
5. Utah (Salt Lake City)
6. Massachusetts
7. The Big Friendly is Oklahoma City, Oklahoma
8. Minnesota, the Land of 10,000 Lakes (which, by the way, has 22,000)
9. It is the quadripoint in the southwestern U.S. where the states of Arizona, Colorado, New Mexico and Utah meet, where visitors can straddle all four states simultaneously.
10. The letter "a", with 21 states

The toothbrush is the number one invention Americans can't live without, ahead of the automobile and personal computer, according to the Lemelson-MIT Invention Index.

PRIVIA

Second Guessing

1. The last Triple Crown winner in horse racing was Affirmed in 1978. Name the horse that finished second in all three races, the only time this has ever happened.

2. Cinco de Mayo is the biggest avocado-eating day in America. What occasion is second?

3. Before 1900, the 984-foot Eiffel Tower was the world's tallest structure. What was second?

4. He won the popular vote, but finished second in the electoral vote and thus lost the presidential race to George W. Bush in 2000.

5. It protects the right of the people to keep and bear arms.

6. Jackie Robinson was the first to break the color barrier in Major League Baseball. Who was the second African American big leaguer?

7. It opened its comedy theatre doors in December, 1959 at 1616 North Wells Street in Chicago.

8. Without using a calculator, are there more or less than 31,556,926 seconds in a year?

9. Art Fleming was the first host of TV's long-running *Jeopardy!* game show. Who was the second?

10. Diana DeGarmo, Katharine McPhee and Lauren Alaina were all second-place finishers in what national competition?

Answers

1. Alydar
2. Super Bowl Sunday
3. The Washington Monument, at 555 feet
4. Al Gore
5. The Second Amendment
6. Larry Doby
7. Second City
8. More or less, there are exactly 31,556,926 seconds in a year.
9. Alex Trebek, since 1984
10. *American Idol*

Thoughts of the Throne

"When somebody follows you twenty blocks to the pharmacy, where they watch you buy toilet paper, you know your life has changed."

– Jennifer Aniston

Time After Time

1. Who conceived the idea of Daylight Saving Time?
2. True or False? The long case clock was known as just that until a song called *My Grandfather's Clock* came along in 1875 and inspired the name change.
3. Levi Hutchins was credited with what startling invention in 1787?
4. True or False? A Friday the 13th occurs once every thirteen months.
5. A simple yes or no will do- Is "in a jiffy" an actual measurement of time?
6. Where is the Great Westminster Clock?
7. Nicknamed for the timepiece they carried during each robbery, this infamous gang had a record heist of $283,000 from a San Diego Bank of America branch in 1980. Can you name them?
8. How long is a fortnight?
9. In 1939, the powers that be figured that time is money, so they instituted the minimum wage. How much was it per hour?
10. William Jonathan Drayton, Jr. is known for having a big timepiece draped around his neck. You know him better by his stage name. What is it?

Answers

1. Benjamin Franklin
2. True
3. The alarm clock
4. False- But you can be sure that whenever the first of any month is on a Sunday, there will be a Friday the 13th that month.
5. Yes- It is 1/100th of a second.
6. In London- Big Ben happens to be the bell inside the tower, not the clock itself.
7. The Stopwatch Gang
8. Fourteen days
9. 25 cents per hour
10. Flavor Flav

The Writing On The Wall

Things are a lot more like they used to be than they are now.

WHAT IN THE WORLD?

1. What country has a capital named after a U.S. president (other than the U.S. itself, of course)?
2. What is the smallest country in the world?
3. What is the only U.S. state to border only one other state?
4. What was the country of Iran formerly called?
5. What city is considered to be the undisputed belly dancing capital of the world?
6. What is the longest river in the world?
7. What country's name comes first, alphabetically speaking?
8. What's the only nation to have a single-colored flag?
9. What country makes the most movies in the world?
10. What city is home to the tallest building in the world?

Answers

1. Liberia- Its capital is Monrovia, named after President James Monroe.
2. Vatican City- With a population less than 800, it occupies just .2 square miles.
3. Maine
4. Persia- And before that, it was called Iran!
5. Cairo, Egypt
6. The Nile, which is 4,135 miles long
7. Afghanistan
8. Libya- Its flag is solid green.
9. India- Its "Bollywood" industry is approximately twice the size of Hollywood's, making close to 1,000 films annually.
10. Dubai- The 2,717-foot tall, 163-story Burj Khalifa was completed there in 2010.

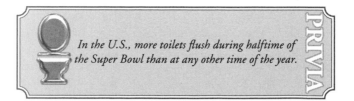

In the U.S., more toilets flush during halftime of the Super Bowl than at any other time of the year.

PRIVIA

Knowing Your ABC's

1. What's the shortest word that uses all five vowels in the English language? (Hint: It's seven letters.)

2. What does the "D" in D-Day stand for?

3. What's the only letter in the alphabet that has three syllables?

4. A, E, I, O, U, H, K, L, M, N, P and W are the twelve letters of what alphabet? (Big hint: It's an alphabet unique to a territory which became an American state in 1959.)

5. On a Bingo card, what letter's column contains a free space?

6. What is the longest word that doesn't contain the vowels a, e, i, o or u? (It's seven letters and is plural.)

7. Only one word ends in the letters "mt". What is it?

8. Name the fictional impish super villain in the *Superman* comic books whose eight-letter name does not have a vowel.

9. What four-letter media giant is headquartered in Bristol, Connecticut?

10. The letter "i" appears six times in what 14-letter word?

Answers

1. Sequoia
2. Day- Hence, in France it's known as J-Jour.
3. W
4. The Hawaiian alphabet
5. N
6. Rhythms
7. Dreamt
8. Mr. Mxyzptlk
9. ESPN
10. Indivisibility

The Writing On The Wall

The Eleventh Commandment:
Thou shall not commit adulthood.

A Sporting Quiz

1. True or False? The official state sport of Maryland is crabbing.
2. To the nearest foot, how far is it from home plate to second base on a big league diamond?
   a) 100' b) 112' c) 120' d) 127'
3. According to the Boat Owners Association of the U.S., what is the most popular name for sailboats?
4. How long does a caddy have to look for a lost ball in pro golf?
5. What is the annual cross-country dog sled race from Anchorage to Nome, Alaska called?
6. What sport's ball is in the shape of a prolate spheroid?
7. A horse named Cilohocla once made the circuit at Florida race tracks. Can you come up with a spirited reason why the horse was so named?
8. What is the only position not named in the famous Abbott and Costello *Who's on First?* routine?
9. A sport called "poona" originated in India. What is it known as today?
10. A Giants-Vikings NFL game was postponed when a snowstorm caused what stadium's roof to collapse in 2010?

Answers

1. False- Believe it or not, it's jousting.
2. D- It's 127 feet, 3 3/8 inches, to be exact.
3. Second Wind
4. Five minutes, so says the Unites States Golf Association rulebook
5. The Iditarod
6. Football
7. Backwards, it spells "alcoholic."
8. Right field- For those keeping score, the pitcher was Tomorrow; the catcher was Today; Who, of course, was on first; What was the second baseman; I Don't Know played third; I Don't Care was the shortstop; Why was in left field and Because played center.
9. Badminton
10. The Metrodome in Minneapolis, Minnesota

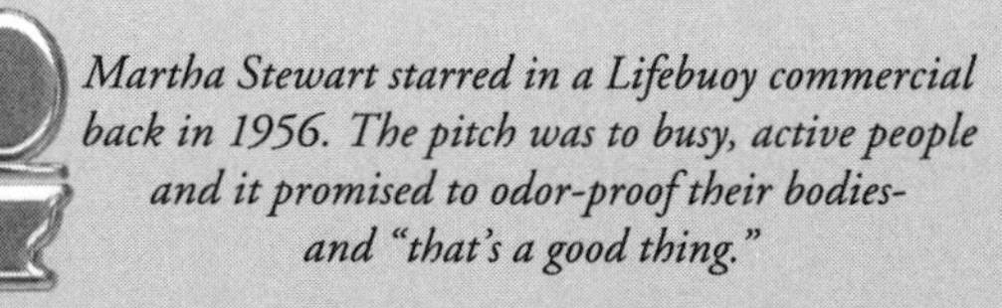

PRIVIA
Martha Stewart starred in a Lifebuoy commercial back in 1956. The pitch was to busy, active people and it promised to odor-proof their bodies- and "that's a good thing."

The "A" List

All of the following solutions begin with the letter A, as in answer. (For names of people, it's their last name starting with the letter A).

1. In 1912, it became the 48th state admitted to the U.S.

2. It is the world's largest waterfall.

3. This Internet service was founded in 1983 as the Control Video Corporation (CVC).

4. Until Seattle Mariners pitcher David Aardsma came around, this Hall of Famer was first on baseball's alphabetical list.

5. A pair of this and a pair of that is known as the dead man's hand because Wild Bill Hickok was supposedly holding it when he was murdered by Jack McCall.

6. Katharine Lee Bates wrote this unofficial national anthem in 1893 after an inspirational climb up Pikes Peak.

7. The U.S. Open tennis tournament is played annually at this venue.

8. She rose from L.A. Lakers cheerleader to Grammy-Award winning recording artist to a TV judge of sorts.

9. This insurance company's duck is enshrined on Madison Avenue's Walk of Fame as one of America's Favorite Advertising Icons.

10. With over 2,000 locations, it is recognized as the world's largest casual dining restaurant chain.

Answers

1. Arizona
2. Angel Falls, in Venezuela, with a height of 3,212 feet
3. AOL
4. Hank Aaron
5. Aces and eights
6. *America the Beautiful*
7. Arthur Ashe Stadium
8. Paula Abdul
9. Aflac
10. Applebee's

Thoughts of the Throne

"If I want to be alone, some place I can write, I can read, I can pray, I can cry, I can do whatever I want - I go to the bathroom."

– Alicia Keys

College Exam

1. What is the oldest college in the U.S.?
2. What colleges did Apple genius Steve Jobs and Microsoft's Bill Gates graduate from?
3. What's the most popular team nickname among four-year colleges?
4. Where would you find Touchdown Jesus?
5. What school did the Delta frats attend in *Animal House*?
6. Who's the only two-time winner of college football's Heisman Trophy?
7. Name the only U.S. president to hold a Ph.D.
8. Harvard freshman Lothrop Withington, Jr. started what nationwide campus fad in late 1938?
9. Big Al the elephant is the mascot of what university?
10. What's that graduation cap with a tassel called?

Answers

1. Harvard University, established in 1636
2. None- Both were college dropouts. Gates attended Harvard and Jobs went to Reed College in Portland, Oregon.
3. Eagles- Tigers is second.
4. On the campus of Notre Dame- It's a mural visible from the school's stadium.
5. Faber College
6. Archie Griffin, of Ohio State, in 1974 and '75
7. Woodrow Wilson, from Johns Hopkins University
8. Goldfish swallowing
9. Alabama
10. A mortarboard

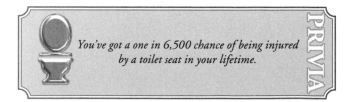

You've got a one in 6,500 chance of being injured by a toilet seat in your lifetime.

PRIVIA

Show Me The Money

1. What do P.T. Barnum, Mark Twain, Walt Disney and Donald Trump have in common?

2. What's the most amount of change you could have without being able to make change for a dollar bill?

3. Of the penny, nickel, dime and quarter, which is the only one where the "head" is facing to the right?

4. True or false? The original motto on U.S. coins was "Mind Your Business."

5. How many ridges are there around the dime?

6. When asked why he was holding out for more money than the president made, Babe Ruth said, "I had a better year than he did." Who was chief executive (hint: the 31st president of the U.S.) at the time?

7. The word "one" appears on the one dollar bill how many times?

8. How many ways can you make change for a dollar?
   a) 23 b) 93 c) 193 d) 293

9. Donald Duck's uncle was the richest duck in the world. What was his name?

10. How many pennies would weigh a pound?
    a) 46 b) 101 c) 181 d) 299

Answers

1. They all went bankrupt at one time or another.
2. $1.19- three quarters, four dimes, and four pennies
3. Honest Abe Lincoln, on the penny, is the only one facing right.
4. True
5. 118
6. Herbert Hoover
7. 8- The key word here is just that, the word "one", not the number.
8. D- 293
9. Scrooge McDuck
10. C- 181

The Writing On The Wall

Sign in restaurant bathroom:

Employees must wash their hands before returning to work.

And a sign underneath it:

You should really wash your hands too.

One for the Ages

1. Popeye is perpetually how old?
2. What is the minimum age for a U.S. senator?
3. In the Disney movie, how old was Sleeping Beauty when she went off into la la land?
4. How old was Elvis Presley when he died?
5. Just how old was John Glenn when he became the oldest astronaut to travel in space?
6. Frances Folsom Cleveland became the youngest First Lady ever when she married President Grover Cleveland in the White House in 1886. What was her age?
7. How old was Albert Einstein when he published his special theory of relativity?
8. There's only one known place in the world that has a maximum voting age. Do you know it?
9. At the age of 76, he was the oldest actor to win the Best Actor Oscar, for his performance in *On Golden Pond*. Name him.
10. How old was Huck Finn in Mark Twain's book?

Answers

1. 34
2. 30
3. 16
4. 42
5. 77- A U.S. senator at the time, he flew aboard the Discovery, which was launched October 29, 1998.
6. 21
7. 26
8. The Holy See, where electing a new Pope is restricted to Cardinals under the age of 80
9. Henry Fonda
10. 13

Thoughts of the Throne

"In a house where there are small children, the bathroom soon takes on the appearance of the Old Curiosity Shop."

– Robert Benchley

Yankee Doodle Dandy

1. You might say this famous figure was a Yankee "Noodle" Dandy. He is said to have introduced macaroni to America and to have had macaroni pie in the White House in 1802. Who is he?

2. Are there more red or white stripes on the American flag?

3. How many rows of stars spangle a U.S. flag?

4. What's the national flower of the United States?

5. What was the name of the horse that Paul Revere rode to warn that the British were coming?

6. Cartoonist Thomas Nast created the donkey and elephant for the Democratic and Republican parties. Nast also created the modern version of Kanakaloka, as he's known in Hawaii. What do we call him throughout the rest of the U.S.?

7. What is the only letter not used in the spelling of any of the 50 states in the U.S.?

8. Who was the first U.S. born citizen to become president? (Hint: He was the eighth president.)

9. What presidential retreat was called Shangri-La until President Eisenhower renamed it after his grandson in 1953?

10. True or False? Benjamin Franklin invented the lightning rod...and swim fins...and the wood stove...and bifocals...and toilet paper.

Answers

1. Thomas Jefferson
2. Reds win, 7-6.
3. 9
4. Rose
5. Brown Beauty
6. Santa Claus
7. Q
8. Martin Van Buren
9. Camp David
10. False- But it was all true up until the last part. Toilet paper was invented by Joseph P. Gayetty in 1857.

The Writing On The Wall

Seen on a stall in a men's bathroom:

My wife follows me everywhere.

Written just below it:

I do not.

'TEN HUT!

1. Who has the higher rank: a U.S. Army captain or a U.S. Navy captain?
2. What Civil War general graduated first in the West Point class of 1829?
3. In the 35-cadet 1861 graduating class at West Point, what number rank was future general George Armstrong Custer?
4. When the occasion arises, the President of the United States receives a 21-gun salute. How many "guns" does the vice-president get?
5. What does the acronym GI stand for?
6. Who was the only person to serve in both the American Revolution and the War of 1812?
7. Name the former Navy SEAL who was a Minnesota governor and pro wrestler.
8. What has been perpetually guarded at Arlington National Cemetery by the U.S. Army since July 2, 1937?
9. If it's 1200 hours in military time, is it noontime or midnight?
10. What former president was a 5-star general?

ANSWERS

1. The Navy captain pulls rank with a level of O-6, the equivalent of an Army colonel. The Army captain is an O-3, equal to that of a Navy lieutenant.
2. Robert E. Lee
3. 35
4. 19
5. Government Issue
6. Andrew Jackson
7. Jesse Ventura
8. The Tomb of the Unknowns
9. Noontime
10. Dwight D. Eisenhower

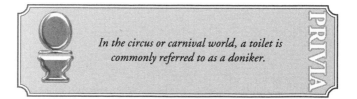

In the circus or carnival world, a toilet is commonly referred to as a doniker.

PRIVIA

Pop Quiz

1. He was Mr. Universe in 1955 and married Jayne Mansfield in 1957. Their daughter became a star on TV's *Law and Order: SVU.* Identify the father and/or daughter.

2. True or false? William Shakespeare was the proud papa of fraternal twins, Romeo and Juliet, born on February 2, 1584.

3. What car, named in honor of Henry Ford's son, was manufactured from 1958-60 and was known as one of the most spectacular failures in the history of the U.S. auto industry?

4. This singer was once known as Luke the Drifter. His son recorded the *Monday Night Football* theme song. Name them.

5. He starred in a number of Hollywood flicks, *Midnight Cowboy* and *Deliverance* among them. Today, you might know him better as the father of a famous movie actress. Who is he?

6. This country singer was best known for *Achy Breaky Heart*, but like his counterpart in the above question, may now be better known as the father of a famous daughter. Name him.

7. Founder Dave Thomas named this fast food restaurant chain after his daughter, whose real name is Melinda.

8. Peyton and Eli followed in their father's footsteps as pro football quarterbacks. What's their pop's first name?

9. Actor Ben Stiller has show biz in his blood. His parents, still going strong today, were formerly a comedy team, with his father getting top billing. What was the duo's name?

10. George Washington, the father of our country, had how many children?

Answers

1. Mickey and Mariska Hargitay
2. False- However, the part about fraternal twins is true. Hamnet and Judith were twin siblings of Shakespeare. Hamnet died before his 12th birthday. Judith lived until the year 1662.
3. The Edsel
4. Hank Williams and Hank Williams, Jr.
5. Jon Voight, whose daughter is Angelina Jolie
6. Billy Ray Cyrus- His daughter, of course, is Miley Cyrus.
7. Wendy's
8. Archie (Manning)
9. Stiller and Meara (Jerry Stiller and Ann Meara)
10. 0

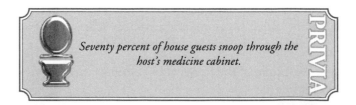

Seventy percent of house guests snoop through the host's medicine cabinet.

TRIVIA

PRIZE PACKAGES

1. The Academy Award of Merit is familiarly known by what friendly name?
2. Who receives the Lady Byng Memorial Trophy for good sportsmanship?
3. The Nobel Peace Prize has been awarded to three sitting U.S. presidents- Barack Obama, Teddy Roosevelt and Woodrow Wilson- and to one former president. Who is he? (Hint- The year was 2002.)
4. She's 15 inches tall from base to tip, weighs 5 pounds and is made of pewter, iron, zinc and gold. She's a daytime and primetime award. Who is she?
5. What awards show was originally held at the Ryman Auditorium but is now presented at the Bridgestone Arena?
6. The Antoinette Perry Awards for Excellence in Theatre is commonly referred to by what name?
7. What team has won the Vince Lombardi Trophy the most times?
8. What is the highest civilian award in the United States?
9. A person of exceptional merit may be declared an Honorary Citizen of the United States by an Act of Congress. Who are the only two people in history to be awarded this distinction during their lifetimes?
10. What school awards the Pulitzer Prize?

Answers

1. The Oscar
2. The National Hockey League's Most Gentlemanly Player
3. Jimmy Carter
4. Emmy- television's prized package
5. The Country Music Association Awards, in Nashville, Tennessee
6. The Tony Awards
7. The Pittsburgh Steelers, winners of six Super Bowls
8. The Presidential Medal of Freedom
9. Winston Churchill (1963) and Mother Teresa (1996)
10. Columbia University- Its journalism school was founded by publisher Joseph Pulitzer from money left in his will.

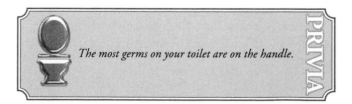

The most germs on your toilet are on the handle.

PRIVIA

Girl Talk

1. Name the only singing group in American Pop history to have twelve straight number one hits.
2. What movie star was named after a building that housed a Cleveland department store?
3. Three women have been Secretary of State in the U.S. Can you name them?
4. What seven-year-old was the youngest host ever of *Saturday Night Live*?
5. This figure skater was the only American to come home with a gold medal from the 1968 Winter Olympics.
6. What television network made its debut on January 1, 2011, replacing the Discovery Health Channel?
7. Who's the only recording artist to ever have five songs surpass the four million-mark in digital sales?
8. She was on its very first cover and has appeared on more covers of *TV Guide* than anyone. Can you name this comic actress?
9. EVOO stands for extra-virgin olive oil and became a dictionary word in 2007 thanks to what TV celebrity cook?
10. What female first did Soviet Valentina Tereshkova achieve in 1963?

Answers

1. The Supremes
2. Halle Berry- She was named after the grand old Halle Building, which originally was home to the Halle Brothers department store.
3. Madeleine Albright, Condoleezza Rice and Hillary Clinton
4. Drew Barrymore, in 1982
5. Peggy Fleming
6. OWN- The Oprah Winfrey Network
7. Katy Perry
8. Lucille Ball
9. Rachael Ray
10. The cosmonaut became the first woman in space.

Thoughts of the Throne

"Life is like a movie- since there aren't any commercial breaks, you have to get up and go to the bathroom in the middle of it."

– Garry Trudeau

Pet Puzzlers

1. Yes or no- Do more than half of America's households own a pet?
2. According to a recent survey, what is the most popular name for a dog?
3. What is it about The Beatles' *A Day in the Life* that can make dogs howl?
4. Dogs have better eyesight, hearing and smelling than we do, but with which sense do humans totally outclass canines?
5. What kind of dog is the only natural toy breed- That is, the only toy breed that wasn't bred down to its small size?
6. What presidential daughter had a pony named Macaroni?
7. What policy does the Vatican have that even the Pope can't break?
8. Which has more bones- a cat or a human?
9. If an animal's eyes face front, what does it mean? And if they are on the side?
10. Which common household pet possesses a Jacobson's organ?

Answers

1. Yes- According to the most recent National Pet Owners Survey, 71.4 million households, or 62%, own at least one pet.
2. Max- Runners-up included Molly, Zach, Sam and Maggie.
3. Paul McCartney recorded a dog whistle at the end of the song. The tone is inaudible to humans, but if played on a good stereo, it makes all pooches within earshot sit up and take notice.
4. Taste- Humans have about 9,000 taste buds, dogs, 1,700. Considering where dogs are always licking, that's probably a blessing.
5. The Chihuahua
6. Caroline Kennedy
7. No Pets- Not even with a security deposit. Pope Benedict XVI's cat Chico has to live back at his place in Tubengen, Germany.
8. A cat has 230 bones, which may explain why dogs chase them so much!
9. As a general rule, an animal with forward-facing eyes is a hunter or carnivore. If the eyes are on the sides, it's a vegetarian and can see hunters approaching from either direction.
10. A cat- The Jacobson's organ is a scent organ in the roof of a cat's mouth.

Candyland

1. What candy did Clarence Crane introduce in 1912, ironically the same year the Titanic sank?

2. "Taste the Rainbow" is the slogan of what candy?

3. Making its debut in 1929, Frank and Ethel Mars named this candy bar after their family horse.

4. Across the pond, "Rowntree's Chocolate Crisp" became the bestselling candy bar in the U.K. What do we call it here?

5. Austrian Leo Hirshfield is credited with bringing this chocolatey, chewy treat to the U.S. in 1896, which he named after his daughter's nickname. Do you know it?

6. What popular candy name is derived from the German word for peppermint?

7. What's the name for that skinny white piece of paper which extends from a Hershey's Kiss?

8. The Y&S candy plant in Lancaster, PA made the longest one ever- 1,200 feet (weighing over 100 pounds), in 1998. Name it.

9. What candy had the color red eliminated from its assortment in 1976 due to health concerns over the dye amaranth, which was a suspected carcinogen? (This was done despite the fact that it did not contain the dye; the action was purely to satisfy worried consumers.)

10. "Sometimes you feel like a nut, sometimes you don't" is the advertising slogan of what candy bar?

Answers

1. Life Savers
2. Skittles
3. Snickers
4. Kit Kat
5. The Tootsie Roll
6. Pez (PfEfferminZ)
7. Plume
8. A licorice twist (Y&S Candies is a subsidiary of Hershey's, which produces Twizzlers, the knotted, twisted licorice candy. Hershey's produces one million miles of them a year!)
9. M&Ms (The color was reinstated in the late 1980s.)
10. Almond Joy

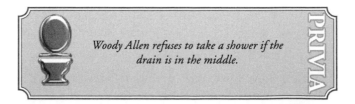

Woody Allen refuses to take a shower if the drain is in the middle.

PRIVIA

MAKEUP TEST

1. What gruesome concoction is made from Karo syrup, food coloring and non-dairy creamer?

2. Florence Graham became famous in the cosmetics world under what name?

3. In the early 1900s, Max Factor specialized in theatrical makeup. What was his first flat-out significant innovation?

4. What popular cosmetic product often contains fish scales?

5. What is the world's best selling (and smelling?) fragrance for men?

6. What cosmetic giant started out as The California Perfume Company in 1886?

7. Back in the 1960s, what would someone expect from QT?

8. Originally called "Baby Gays", by what name do we refer to them nowadays?

9. What is a blepharoplasty?

10. Which major cosmetics firm was named partially for petroleum jelly?

Answers

1. Fake movie blood- Exact recipes vary, but this is the basic formula. Of course in the days of black and white, they could get away with just using chocolate syrup.

2. Elizabeth Arden

3. Pancake makeup

4. Lipstick- Look for ones that list "pearl essence" as an ingredient. It also turns up in nail polish. It's made of mechanically de-scaled herring.

5. Armani

6. Avon

7. "You get a quick tan with QT", the jingle went. It was applied to the skin for a sunless tan in a few hours. It was introduced by Coppertone but wasn't quite perfected, with the most common complaint being carrot orange palms.

8. Q-Tips

9. An upper or lower eyelid lift

10. Maybelline- T.L. Williams, the company founder, named it after his sister Maybel and Vaseline.

You Betcha

1. What do you call the dots on dice?
2. In what card game do you have "the flop", "the turn" and "the river"?
3. San Francisco's Charles Fey introduced what popular gambling innovation in 1899?
4. Which famous Las Vegas casino was named for a showgirl's legs?
5. True or False? As of 2010, playing pinball was still illegal in Beacon, New York.
6. The odds of getting this are 649,740 to 1. What is it?
7. Name the three legs, in order of which they are run, of horse racing's Triple Crown.
8. Who financed his political career with the tens of thousands of dollars he won playing poker in the South Pacific during World War II?
9. What's odd about the sum of all the numbers on the roulette wheel?
10. What do the opposite sides of a dice cube always add up to?

Answers

1. Pips
2. Texas Hold 'em
3. The first slot machine, "Liberty Bell"
4. Bugsy Siegel named the Flamingo for the long legs of Virginia Hill, his statuesque girlfriend. He felt that the Flamingo was a bit classier than the Va Va Va Voom.
5. True
6. A royal flush
7. The Kentucky Derby, The Preakness, and The Belmont Stakes
8. Richard Nixon
9. They add up to 666 – a number that many attribute to Satan.
10. 7

Thoughts of the Throne

"When a child is locked in the bathroom with water running and he says he's doing nothing, but the dog is barking, call 911."

– Erma Bombeck

Potty-Pourri

1. What are Great White, Mortgage Lifter, Gold Dust, Stupice and Tigrella?
2. Charles Jung made his fortune on this cookie, which he invented in 1918.
3. If you just made a fillip, what did you do? (Hint: This one's a snap!)
4. "Praised be our Lord Jesus Christ! With my prayers and blessings, Benedictus XV"… With that papal announcement, on June 28, 2011, Pope Benedict XV communicated like no other pope before him. How so?
5. You probably know that The Blue Angels are the U.S. Navy's aerial acrobatic team, but who are the Red Arrows?
6. Eileen Regina Edwards is better known to music fans as... ?
7. In April of 1964, the U.S. Post Office assigned the zip code 20252 to what popular figure?
8. What long-running space vehicle program came to an end in 2011?
9. This 007 star was the oldest-ever to win *People Magazine's* "Sexiest Man Alive" award. Who is he?
10. True or False? A nun was once the Mayor of Dubuque, Iowa.

Answers

1. Varieties of tomatoes
2. The fortune cookie, invented right here in the good old USA
3. Snapped your fingers.
4. He became the first pope to tweet.
5. The RAF's precision flight team
6. Shania Twain
7. Smokey Bear
8. The Space Shuttle
9. Sean Connery, at 59, in 1989
10. True- Sister Carolyn Farrell was elected mayor in 1980.

The Writing On The Wall

Actual graffiti in the Microsoft bathroom:

Do Not Flush Mouse Pads Down The Toilet

To Flush, Press Handle. You Do Not Need To Hold Control, Alt, And Delete At The Same Time.

FOOD FOR THOUGHT

1. Sweets lovers everywhere owe a debt of gratitude to Daniel Peter for what invention?

2. This common food additive is still giving consumers a fair shake, as it hasn't risen dramatically in price over the past 150 years.

3. SPAM is unwelcome in our email, a subject of one of Monty Python's most famous bits and the world's most enduring mystery meat. You've heard the name for years, but what do the letters stand for?

4. According to the U.S. Department of Agriculture, has the consumption of beer gone up or down the past 20 years?

5. What popular pastry was originally marketed as Little Shortcake Fingers?

6. Vanilla comes from:
   a) bushes b) trees c) vines d) orchids

7. Wonder Bread rocked the grocery shelves with this innovation in 1930.

8. How did the onion, of all things, keep them honest in ancient Egypt?

9. In Italy, what cheese is often made with water buffalo milk?

10. What gum's distinctive flavor comes from vanilla, wintergreen and a form of cinnamon called cassis?

Answers

1. He invented milk chocolate with help from Henri Nestle. If oil lamps hadn't forced a dim future upon his candle-making business, we might not have his delicious invention.
2. Table salt, still giving consumers a fair shake
3. Shoulder of Pork and Ham
4. Up, some 100%! Americans guzzle over $25 billion worth a year.
5. Twinkies- Before the current name, they were known as "Twinkie Fingers".
6. D- The expensive flavor comes from pods from orchids.
7. Sliced bread- Customers thought it was the greatest thing since, well, itself!
8. When ancient Egyptian leaders took an oath of office, they placed their right hand on an onion. Ever since, cutting onions has caused many people to swear an oath!
9. Mozzarella
10. Bubble gum

Vocabulary Vexers

1. If your musical tastes were corybantic, would you more likely attend the symphony or a rock concert?
2. If you've ever watched late night television, you've almost certainly seen an eccedentesiast. How can you spot them?
3. While compiling this book, we indulged in a veritable orgy of floccinaucinihilipilification. What do you think we were doing?
4. If you woke up in a state of euneirophrenia, would you scream for your medication or just lay back and enjoy it?
5. If you were gambrinous, would you be more likely to go to the bedroom, the kitchen, the bathroom or the laundry room?
6. If someone called you a blatteroon, should you take it as a compliment?
7. Often after a big party, the hostess finds a culacino or two. Are any of her guests likely to call to ask if they left one behind?
8. Many workers in Las Vegas lead a lychnobite existence. True or False?
9. If you're a quinquagenarian, have you hit puberty yet?
10. You, of course, know where to find your glabella. It's written all over your face. Look in a mirror and browse around and it will suddenly hit you right between the eyes. What is it?

Answers

1. A rock concert- Corybantic means wild and frenzied.
2. It's anyone with a phony, fake or put-on smile.
3. Categorizing something as useless or trivial
4. Enjoy! It means awakening in a blissful state, as if from a pleasant dream.
5. As it means full of beer, hopefully you would choose the bathroom before any of the others.
6. No. A blatteroon talks on and on incessantly, an unfortunate occupational hazard for radio talk show hosts, insurance salesmen and trivia writers.
7. No. They are the marks left on furniture from wet glasses. That's what the coasters are for, people!
8. True. They sleep in the daytime and work at night.
9. Yes- It means you're between the ages of 50-60.
10. It's the smooth, hairless patch most people have between their eyebrows.

More than 50% of people who have laptops admit to having checked their e-mails in the bathroom.

PRIVIA

NOT JUST A PRETTY FACE

Match the following celebrities with their degrees.
All are earned rather than honorary.

1. John Cleese
2. Lisa Kudrow
3. Katherine Hepburn
4. Mayim Bialik
5. Rowan Atkinson
6. Conan O'Brien
7. Dolph Lundgren
8. Graham Chapman
9. Jimmy Stewart
10. Maggie Gyllenhaal

a) Neuroscience
b) Psychology
c) American Literature
d) Electrical engineer
e) Law
f) Biology
g) Architecture
h) Eastern Religions
i) Chemical engineer
j) Medicine

Answers

1. E- John Cleese got his degree from Cambridge University.
2. F- Lisa Kudrow went to Vassar to attain her degree.
3. B- Katherine Hepburn received her psychology degree from Bryn Mawr.
4. A- Mayim Bialik has her Ph.D in neuroscience.
5. D- Rowan Atkinson graduated from Oxford with his degree in electrical engineering.
6. C- Conan O'Brien attended Harvard, where he earned his degrees in American Lit and History.
7. I- Dolph Lundgren was a graduate from the Royal Institute of Technology in Sweden.
8. J- Graham Chapman went to Cambridge for his medical degree.
9. G- Jimmy Stewart worked his way through Princeton to wind up with a degree in architecture.
10. H- Maggie Gyllenhaal attended Columbia for her degree in Eastern Religions.

Just in case you were wondering, we weren't able to find the Six Degrees *of Kevin Bacon.*

Let's Play Doctor

1. Theodor Geisel is better known by what name?
2. "Your name is mud" comes from Dr. Samuel Mudd, who was vilified by the American people for treating what patient?
3. True or false? During Civil War days, an undertaker was called "doctor".
4. What is the last name of TV's Dr. Phil?
5. What is the first name of TV's Dr. Oz?
6. The creator of superhero Wonder Woman also invented the lie detector test. Honest. His name is:
   a) Dr. William Moulton Marston b) Dr. Livingstone
   c) Dr. Benjamin Spock d) Dr. Ruth
7. Hugh Laurie plays the central character in what television medical drama?
8. Who is the Surgeon General in the United States?
9. Was there really a podiatrist named Dr. Scholl?
10. Dr. Vinny Boom Bots was the personal physician of what comedian?

ANSWERS

1. Dr. Seuss
2. Abraham Lincoln's assassin, John Wilkes Booth
3. True
4. McGraw
5. Mehmet
6. A
7. *House*
8. Dr. Regina Benjamin
9. Yes- William Mathias Scholl founded Dr. Scholl's foot care and product company in 1906.
10. Rodney Dangerfield, who just never got any respect ("When I was born, the doctor took one look at my face, turned me over and said, 'Look, twins!'")

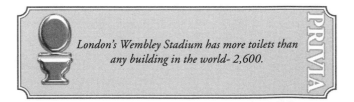

London's Wembley Stadium has more toilets than any building in the world- 2,600.

TRIVIA

Comically Speaking

1. What illuminating character did Ryan Reynolds play in the 2011 blockbuster movie that was made after a comic of the same name?
2. Riverdale High's Kevin is the first character in the long history of *Archie* comic books to be what?
3. Prince Orin was abandoned as an infant for having blond hair that literally put The Curse Of Kordax upon his head. What superhero did the young man grow up to be?
4. It sold for $1.5 million, making it the world's most expensive comic book. (Hint: It was written by Jerry Siegel and illustrated by Joe Shuster.)
5. What is the attractive alter ego of Eric Lensherr?
6. Which superhero comic featured an "inaugural" appearance by President Obama?
7. What movie star's comic book collection was sold at an auction for $1.68 million to help alleviate his financial woes?
8. Stanley Martin Lieber is better known to comic book fans as... ?
9. What day of the year is Superman's birthday?
10. Who were Bruce Wayne and Dick Grayson?

Answers

1. He played the title character in *The Green Lantern.*
2. Gay
3. Aquaman
4. DC *Action Comics* #1, June 1938, featuring the world's first look at Superman
5. Magneto
6. Marvel's *Spider-man*
7. Nicholas Cage- That figure didn't even include his extremely valuable copy of DC *Action Comics* #1, which was stolen in 2000 and recovered in 2011.
8. Stan Lee
9. February 29
10. Batman and Robin, respectively

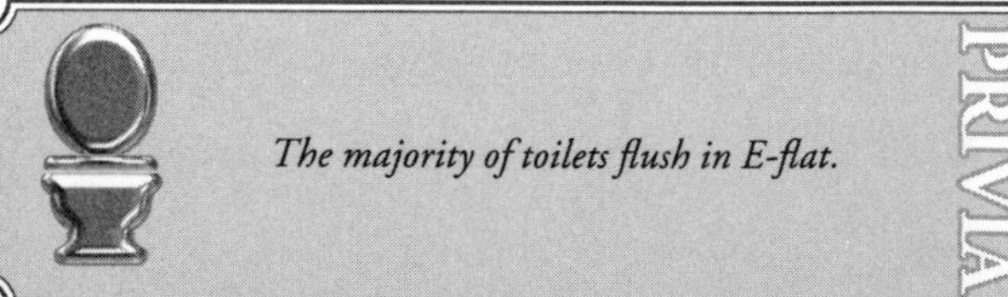

PRIVIA
The majority of toilets flush in E-flat.

Screen Test

1. Here's one to break the ice: What popular reality show was based out of Yellowknife, Northwest Territories, Canada?

2. What 2006 Samuel L. Jackson movie was a huge hit before it was even made due to immense Internet buzz?

3. If you give a hoot about *Harry Potter* films and know who's who, you should know Hedwig. What is his relationship with Harry?

4. This series went off the air in 1999 after a ten-year run on cable TV. Fans of this comedy were called "Misties".

5. Kelsey Grammer played the character Frasier Crane for 20 years on three different sitcoms. Cheers to you if you can name all three.

6. *The Merry Go Round Broke Down* was used as the theme for a long-running cartoon series that is still popular today. Name that 'toon!

7. In 1989, Edith Fore became a celebrity on the basis of her appearance on TV commercials and her catchphrase, which became a national sensation. What line was she famous for?

8. Which TV funnyman had his hair cut as per President Obama's direct order while entertaining in Iraq?

9. Justin Long and John Hodgman played which friendly competitors in a popular series of high tech ads?

10. When this cable network found that it couldn't trademark its well-known name, it changed the spelling to a new word that was pronounced the same.

Answers

1. *Ice Road Truckers*
2. *Snakes on a Plane*
3. He's Potter's pet owl.
4. *Mystery Science Theater 3000,* or *MST3K,* as the Misties would call it. The show has partially been reborn on the Internet with original cast members on Rifftrax.com and CinematicTitanic.com.
5. *Cheers, Frasier* and a guest shot on *Wings.*
6. *Looney Tunes*
7. "I've fallen and I can't get up!"
8. Steven Colbert- The order was carried out by four star general Ray Odierno.
9. Mac and PC
10. The Sci Fi Channel changed its name to Syfy

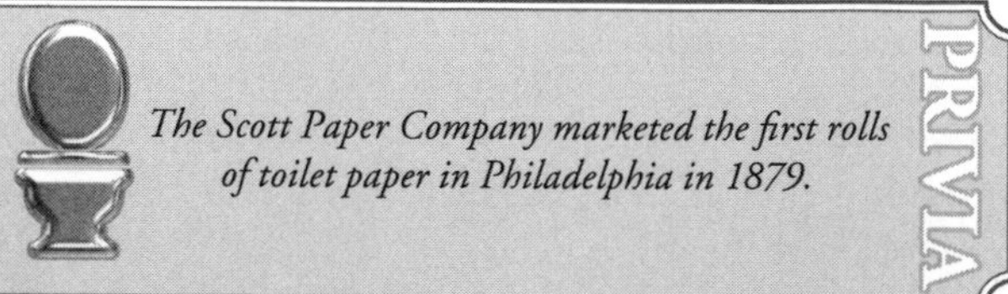

The Scott Paper Company marketed the first rolls of toilet paper in Philadelphia in 1879.

Science Fiction or Fact?

1. The water recycling system on the International Space Station recycles 93% of the astronauts' bodily waste fluid back into drinking water. *Fiction or Fact?*

2. Limited cold fusion has reportedly been achieved by placing uranium electrodes into salted potatoes in an extreme magnetic field and then firing a laser at them. *Fiction or Fact?*

3. Sharks seem to become less aggressive and more inquisitive when they hear AC/DC music, particularly *Back In Black* and *Shook Me All Night Long. Fiction or Fact?*

4. Two lovers engaging in a real first-class smackeroo will likely emerge from the lip lock with dilated pupils. *Fiction or Fact?*

5. Red diamonds can form when lightning strikes a deeply buried piece of coal. *Fiction or Fact?*

6. A moderate sunburn damages blood vessels in the skin so badly that they can take up to 15 months to heal. *Fiction or Fact?*

7. The oldest tree in the world is over 9,500 years old. *Fiction or Fact?*

8. Geologically speaking, seafloors are the oldest pieces of the Earth's crust, with the oldest in the western Pacific being about four billion years old. *Fiction or Fact?*

9. It takes longer to boil water at the bottom of a coal mine than at the top of a mountain. *Fiction or Fact?*

10. The modern lawn sprinkler was actually invented in ancient times as a primitive steam engine. *Fiction or Fact?*

Answers

1. Fact- Cheers everyone!
2. Fiction
3. Fact
4. Fact
5. Fiction
6. Fact
7. Fact- It's a spruce growing in Sweden.
8. Fiction- The seafloor gets recycled fairly fast, with the oldest being about 200 million years old.
9. Fact- The effect is due to increased air pressure.
10. Fact- It was invented by Hero, a Greek engineer, about 2,000 years ago.

The Writing On The Wall

Under a sign that said: "Employees Must Wash Hands"

I waited and waited, but I finally washed them myself

A Royal Flush of Facts

Up to this point it's been business as usual. We've been plumbing your knowledge and draining your brain, but by now you've done your duty. So just sit back and have fun with some fascinating and frivolous factoids.

More than half of Americans can name the Three Stooges, but less than 17% can name three U.S. Supreme Court judges.

•

A party boat with sixty people once capsized in Texas when everyone on board rushed to one side as the boat passed a nude beach.

•

35% of Americans get something to eat at a fast food restaurant at least once a week.

•

More Americans choke on the toothpick than any other object.

•

Donald Duck was once banned in Finland because he didn't wear any pants.

Guinness World Records holds a world record of its own. It is the best-selling copyrighted book series of all-time.

•

A NASCAR fan once sent over 500,000 e-mails to the FOX network for televising a baseball game instead of a scheduled race.

•

The tallest snowman on record was higher than a 12-story building.

•

In Japan, there are watermelons shaped like pyramids.

•

Stefani Joanne Angelina Germanotta began learning to play piano at the age of four and wrote her first piano ballad at 13, long before she became known as Lady Gaga.

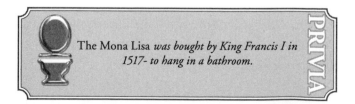

The Mona Lisa *was bought by King Francis I in 1517- to hang in a bathroom.*

PRIVIA

The lint in your belly button is made of hair, dead skin cells and clothing fiber.

•

YouTube was created by Steve Charin, Chad Hurley and Jawed Karim in 2005, after Karim became frustrated when he couldn't easily locate a video clip of Janet Jackson's Super Bowl halftime wardrobe malfunction.

•

If you have a tremendous fear of ghosts, you have phasmophobia.

•

An alligator can live to be 80 years old.

•

Dolphins can hear underwater sounds 15 miles away.

•

Owls are unable to move their eyeballs.

•

If you're the average American, you'll drive about 627,000 miles in your lifetime.

The most expensive thing ever sold on eBay was a $168 million yacht.

•

Chewing gum burns about 11 calories per hour.

•

In the U.S., there are more plastic flamingos than real ones.

•

The parachute was invented before the airplane.

•

Olympic gold medals are more than 90% silver.

•

There are more sheep in New Zealand than people.

•

It's considered good luck to wear yellow underwear on New Year's Day in Peru.

The Writing On The Wall

Deja Moo : The feeling you've heard this bull before !

Yes, you can get cell phone reception at the top of Mt. Everest.

•

Justin Timberlake began his singing career on *Star Search* as Justin Randall.

•

In 1976, Bruce Springsteen was nabbed by security guards when he tried to scale the wall outside of Graceland to meet Elvis.

•

Gorillas burp when they are happy.

•

Traveling non-stop, a snail would take about 220 hours to crawl a mile.

•

A crocodile cannot stick out its tongue.

•

Your skin can turn orange if you eat too many carrots.

•

It is impossible to breathe and swallow at the same time.

Your hair grows faster in warm weather.

•

Toyota was founded in 1937 by the Toyoda family. The name is spelled differently because Toyota with a "t" is thought to have a luckier number of brush strokes when written in Japanese.

•

Your average dream lasts about 20 minutes.

•

A camel can gulp down 500 cups of water in 10 minutes.

•

For some reason, men get the hiccups more than women.

•

Neil Armstrong, the first man on the moon, left his space boots there.

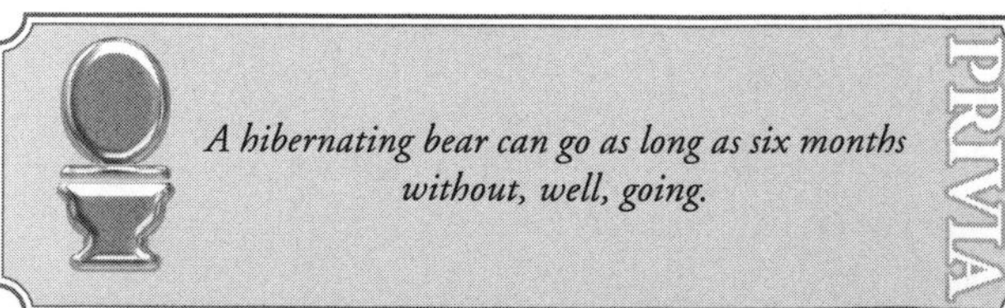

A hibernating bear can go as long as six months without, well, going.

It is possible to smell scents when you dream.

•

The very first e-mail was sent in 1971.

•

A group of blue jays is called a party.

•

Sharks have no bones.

•

Crocodiles are not able to chew.

•

White flamingos can turn pink from eating shrimp.

•

M&M's- "They melt in your mouth, not in your hands" –were developed so that soldiers wouldn't get sticky fingers when they ate chocolate.

•

A litter of kittens is also known as a kindle.

•

When the bald eagle was named, the word "bald" meant "white."

There are more text messages sent each day than there are people in the world.

•

Cross a whale and a dolphin and you get a wholphin.

•

Squirrels don't exist in Australia.

•

In 2010, someone paid $1.2 million for John Lennon's handwritten lyrics for *A Day in the Life.*

•

Kirstie Alley won $6,000 on TV's *Match Game* in 1979.

•

"The answer is yes!" That was *Jeopardy!* host Alex Trebek's reply when he and his wife, Jean Currivan, exchanged wedding vows.

THE WRITING ON THE WALL

Deja Moo : The feeling you've heard this bull before !

Sean "Diddy" Combs and Johnny Depp both suffer from coulrophobia- a fear of clowns.

•

C-SPAN stands for Cable-Satellite Public Affairs Network.

•

Motorola's Dr. Martin Cooper made the very first cell phone call on the streets of New York City in 1973.

•

When 7-Eleven opened its doors in 1927, it was known as Tote'm Stores.

•

Bernie Madoff's 55-foot yacht was named Bull.

•

The typical American woman averages five haircuts a year. About 25% of them say they have cried after a bad haircut.

•

The face on the Statue of Liberty is bigger than Abraham Lincoln's Mt. Rushmore mug.

Americans devour 47 billion hamburgers a year.

•

99 out of 100 tornadoes rotate counterclockwise in the Northern Hemisphere.

•

Identical twins are not 100% identical. They have different fingerprints.

•

If you've ever had brain freeze, medically speaking, you suffered from sphenopalatineganglioneuralgia.

•

Orangutans have been known to make umbrellas out of branches.

•

It'll take you 40 minutes to boil an ostrich egg and will cost you 2,000 calories if you eat it.

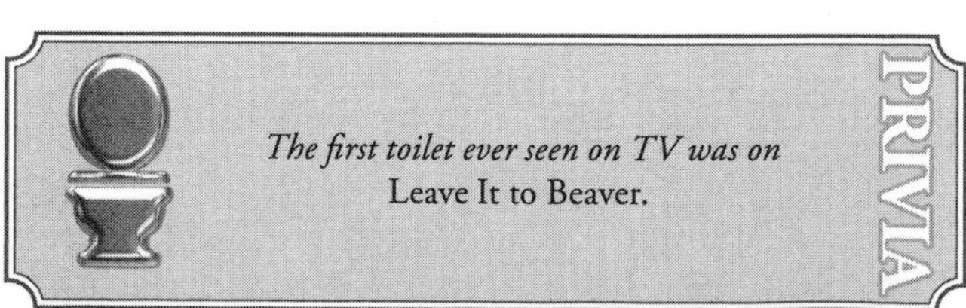

The first toilet ever seen on TV was on Leave It to Beaver.

King Henry VIII was almost 400 pounds when he died.

•

New York City has 572 miles of shoreline.

•

Clean snow doesn't melt as fast as dirty snow.

•

86% of dads attend the birth of their children.

•

The minimum height for an American astronaut is 4' 10 ½".

•

Despite inflation, Monopoly board values are the same today as they were in 1935.

•

In addition to orange, carrots can be purple, red, white or yellow.

•

Two-thirds of the world's eggplant is grown in the Garden State, New Jersey.

George Washington owned a brewery on the grounds of Mt. Vernon.

•

There are 99 bodies of water named Mud Lake in Minnesota.

•

Sandra Bullock is allergic to horses.

•

Seinfeld minutiae: In eight years, Cosmo Kramer went through Jerry Seinfeld's apartment door 284 times.

•

Baboons can't toss a ball overhand.

•

Ben Franklin gave guitar lessons.

The Writing On The Wall

I became self-employed and I still have a jerk for a boss.

Dr. Seuss was the first to use the word "nerd" in his 1950 book *If I Ran the Zoo.*

•

Ham Gravy was Olive Oyl's boyfriend before Popeye.

•

On average, it takes 2,893 licks to get to the center of the Tootsie Pop.

•

Simply reading about yawning will be enough to make many people yawn.

•

The working title of The Beatles song *With a Little Help from My Friends* was *Bad Finger Boogie.*

•

They were introduced in 1912, and some 500 billion creme-filled sandwiches later, Oreos are known as the best-selling cookie in the world.

•

The infinity symbol is called a "lemniscate."

The average coffee drinker will down 70,000 cups in a lifetime.

•

Light bulb inventor Thomas Edison was afraid of the dark.

•

On the Monopoly game board, that character behind bars is Jake the Jailbird.

•

Right-handed people are more likely to scratch with their left hand and vice-versa.

•

If you ate like a bird, you'd be eating twice your weight every day, as many of our fine-feathered friends do.

•

Whenever you sneeze, your heart stops.

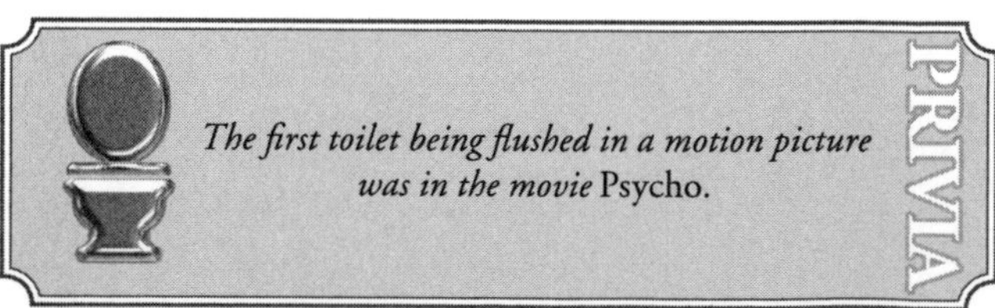

The first toilet being flushed in a motion picture was in the movie Psycho.

Rabbits have been clocked as fast as 47 mph.

•

There are more than twice as many pigs as people in Denmark.

•

In his leaner years, Matt Damon would break-dance for money in Harvard Square.

•

An Amish man who has a beard is a married man.

•

Disney's Space Mountain in Paris reaches a maximum speed of 43 mph, the fastest of all the Mickey Mouse parks.

•

The word "Sunday" does not appear in *The Bible.*

•

Burger King is called Hungry Jack's in Australia.

•

More people have seen David Copperfield perform live than any other entertainer in the world.

Henry Ford was the first American to be worth a billion dollars.

•

Vanna White, famed for her letter-turning role on *Wheel of Fortune*, deserves some applause for finding her way into the *Guinness Book* as the world's most frequent clapper.

•

When Colgate toothpaste was first made, it came in a jar.

•

Grey's Anatomy star Patrick Dempsey's career began as a juggling unicycle-riding clown.

•

Charles Lindbergh took a Felix the Cat doll with him on his first transatlantic flight.

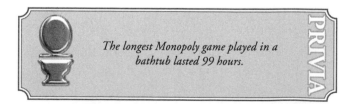

The longest Monopoly game played in a bathtub lasted 99 hours.

More gold is used in the United States to make class rings than for anything else.

•

Einstein was ten years old before he learned to read.

•

The Turtles were the first rock band to play at the White House, in 1969, at Trisha Nixon's Masque Ball.

•

One in three dog owners say they've talked to their pooch on the phone.

•

Matthew Perry lost part of his middle finger on his right hand due to a door-shutting accident.

•

The four least-used letters of the alphabet are Q, X, Z and J.

•

Two states are the most "neighborly" of all. Missouri and Tennessee both touch on eight other states.

THE BATHROOM LIBRARY

The Bathroom Baseball Book

•

The Bathroom Bloopers Book

•

The Bathroom Brain Teasers Book

•

The Bathroom Football Book

•

The Bathroom Funny Pages

•

The Bathroom Game Book

•

The Bathroom Golf Book

•

The Bathroom Joke Book

•

The Bathroom LOL Book

•

The Bathroom Rock 'n Roll Book

•

The Bathroom Sports Pages

•

The Bathroom Sports Quiz Book

•

The Bathroom Trivia Digest

•

The Bathroom Trivia Quiz Book